Times Tables Tutor

(for ages 7-11)

Managing Editors: Simon Melhuish and Sarah Wells
Series Editor: Nikole G Bamford
Designer: Linley J Clode

Published by
The Lagoon Group
PO Box 311, KT2 5QW, UK
PO Box 990676, Boston, MA 02199, USA

ISBN: 1904797016

www.thelagoongroup.com

Printed in China

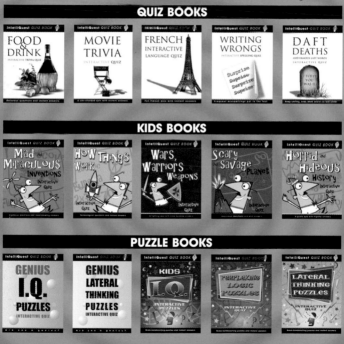

IntelliQuest

UNIQUE BOOK CODE	016

Instructions

First of all make sure you have a Quizmo —

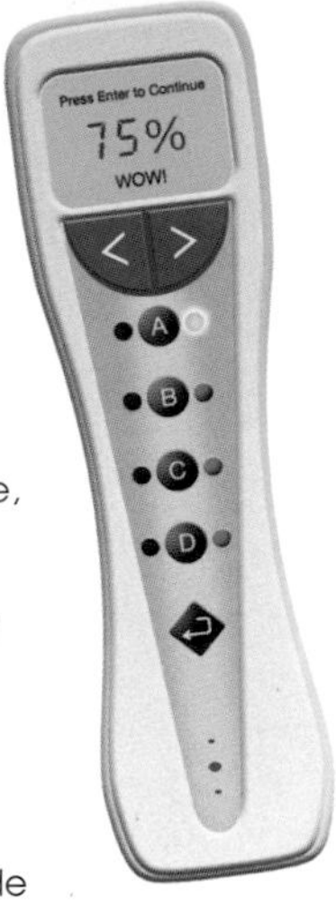

Find the book's unique code (this appears at the top of this page). Use the < and > buttons to scroll to this number on the Quizmo screen. Press the ↵ button to enter the code, and you're ready to go.

Use the < > scroll buttons to select the question number you want to answer. Press the A, B, C, or D button to enter your chosen answer.

If you are correct the green light beside the button you pressed will flash. You can then use the scroll button to move on to another question.

If your answer is incorrect, the red light beside the button you pressed will flash.

Don't worry, you can try again and again until you have the correct answer, OR move on to another question. (Beware: the more times you guess incorrectly, the lower your final percentage score will be!)

You can finish the quiz at any point — just press the button to find out your score and rank as follows:

75% or above	You're a mathematical brainbox!
50% — 74%	You're a whizz with numbers.
25% — 49%	Keep trying — it's the only way.
Less than 25%	Stick with it and you'll soon be up to speed.

If you do press the button to find out your score, this will end your session and you will have to use the to start again!

HAVE FUN!

2 TIMES TABLES

Here's stuff you know already so you should be able to speed through these.

$1 \times 2 = 2$

$2 \times 2 = 4$

$3 \times 2 = 6$

$4 \times 2 = 8$

$5 \times 2 = 10$

$6 \times 2 = 12$

$7 \times 2 = 14$

$8 \times 2 = 16$

$9 \times 2 = 18$

$10 \times 2 = 20$

$11 \times 2 = 22$

$12 \times 2 = 24$

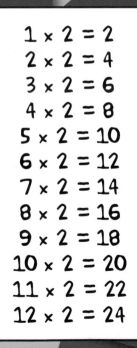

2 TIMES TABLES

001

12 × 2 =

A 24 B 14 C 12 D 28

002

2 × 11 =

A 22 B 11 C 20 D 32

003

3 × 2 =

A 3 B 2 C 5 D 6

004

2 × 7 =

A 14 B 2 C 7 D 16

005

5 × 2 =

A 2 B 5 C 10 D 7

006

2 × 6 =

A 12 B 2 C 6 D 2

2 TIMES TABLES

007

$8 \times 2 =$

A 12 B 16 C 14 D 19

008

$1 \times 2 =$

A 1 B 3 C 4 D 2

009

$2 \times 9 =$

A 11 B 18 C 16 D 19

010

$10 \times 2 =$

A 12 B 10 C 20 D 22

011

$4 \times 2 =$

A 2 B 6 C 4 D 8

012

$2 \times 2 =$

A 2 B 22 C 3 D 4

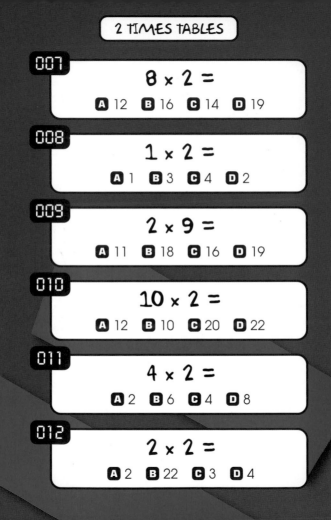

3 TIMES TABLES

You know your 3 Times Table. Look at it again and you'll be able to scoot through the questions afterwards!

$1 \times 3 = 3$
$2 \times 3 = 6$
$3 \times 3 = 9$
$4 \times 3 = 12$
$5 \times 3 = 15$
$6 \times 3 = 18$
$7 \times 3 = 21$
$8 \times 3 = 24$
$9 \times 3 = 27$
$10 \times 3 = 30$
$11 \times 3 = 33$
$12 \times 3 = 36$

3 TIMES TABLES

013

$1 \times 3 =$

A 3   B 1   C 4   D 6

014

$7 \times 3 =$

A 14   B 17   C 23   D 21

015

$3 \times 6 =$

A 18   B 24   C 20   D 12

016

$2 \times 3 =$

A 2   B 6   C 3   D 5

017

$3 \times 11 =$

A 11   B 33   C 22   D 32

018

$4 \times 3 =$

A 12   B 3   C 7   D 4

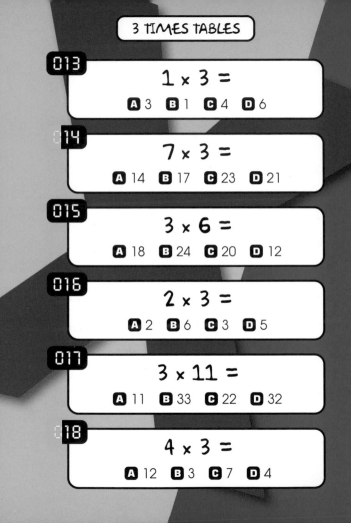

3 TIMES TABLES

019

$3 \times 3 =$

A 3 B 9 C 6 D 12

020

$5 \times 3 =$

A 5 B 8 C 25 D 15

021

$3 \times 8 =$

A 16 B 18 C 24 D 26

022

$9 \times 3 =$

A 24 B 27 C 21 D 19

023

$3 \times 10 =$

A 10 B 20 C 30 D 35

024

$12 \times 3 =$

A 30 B 36 C 34 D 32

4 TIMES TABLES

Another easy one for you. Take a quick look and you'll be able to breeze through the questions.

$1 \times 4 = 4$
$2 \times 4 = 8$
$3 \times 4 = 12$
$4 \times 4 = 16$
$5 \times 4 = 20$
$6 \times 4 = 24$
$7 \times 4 = 28$
$8 \times 4 = 32$
$9 \times 4 = 36$
$10 \times 4 = 40$
$11 \times 4 = 44$
$12 \times 4 = 48$

4 TIMES TABLES

025

$5 \times 4 =$

A 10 B 20 C 24 D 25

026

$1 \times 4 =$

A 1 B 2 C 4 D 14

027

$10 \times 4 =$

A 20 B 40 C 45 D 50

028

$4 \times 4 =$

A 8 B 12 C 16 D 4

029

$4 \times 6 =$

A 12 B 18 C 28 D 24

030

$4 \times 12 =$

A 52 B 44 C 48 D 40

4 TIMES TABLES

031

$7 \times 4 =$

A 28 B 24 C 29 D 32

032

$4 \times 3 =$

A 3 B 7 C 12 D 16

033

$4 \times 8 =$

A 28 B 32 C 26 D 24

034

$9 \times 4 =$

A 36 B 32 C 34 D 28

035

$2 \times 4 =$

A 2 B 4 C 8 D 12

036

$11 \times 4 =$

A 36 B 44 C 40 D 48

5 TIMES TABLES

Here's the 5 Times Table. You should be very familiar with these so you can race through the questions.

$1 \times 5 = 5$
$2 \times 5 = 10$
$3 \times 5 = 15$
$4 \times 5 = 20$
$5 \times 5 = 25$
$6 \times 5 = 30$
$7 \times 5 = 35$
$8 \times 5 = 40$
$9 \times 5 = 45$
$10 \times 5 = 50$
$11 \times 5 = 55$
$12 \times 5 = 60$

5 TIMES TABLES

037

$6 \times 5 =$

A 25 B 40 C 35 D 30

038

$1 \times 5 =$

A 5 B 3 C 1 D 6

039

$12 \times 5 =$

A 65 B 60 C 70 D 75

040

$3 \times 5 =$

A 18 B 15 C 13 D 12

041

$5 \times 4 =$

A 20 B 18 C 16 D 14

042

$7 \times 5 =$

A 40 B 35 C 45 D 42

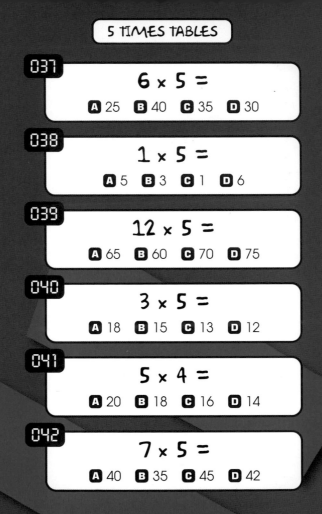

5 TIMES TABLES

043

$5 \times 5 =$

A 15 B 25 C 20 D 35

044

$2 \times 5 =$

A 5 B 7 C 10 D 2

045

$8 \times 5 =$

A 35 B 48 C 45 D 40

046

$5 \times 9 =$

A 35 B 40 C 45 D 30

047

$10 \times 5 =$

A 15 B 45 C 50 D 55

048

$11 \times 5 =$

A 55 B 45 C 60 D 65

10 TIMES TABLES

Here's another one you know well! Take another look at the 10 Times Table and answer the questions afterwards as quickly as possible!

$1 \times 10 = 10$
$2 \times 10 = 20$
$3 \times 10 = 30$
$4 \times 10 = 40$
$5 \times 10 = 50$
$6 \times 10 = 60$
$7 \times 10 = 70$
$8 \times 10 = 80$
$9 \times 10 = 90$
$10 \times 10 = 100$
$11 \times 10 = 110$
$12 \times 10 = 120$

10 TIMES TABLES

049

$9 \times 10 =$

A 109 B 91 C 99 D 90

050

$10 \times 5 =$

A 55 B 51 C 5 D 50

051

$2 \times 10 =$

A 2 B 20 C 10 D 22

052

$10 \times 8 =$

A 81 B 80 C 88 D 89

053

$3 \times 10 =$

A 33 B 27 C 30 D 3

054

$12 \times 10 =$

A 110 B 120 C 112 D 121

10 TIMES TABLES

055

$11 \times 10 =$

A 101 B 112 C 111 D 110

056

$10 \times 4 =$

A 4 B 44 C 40 D 41

057

$6 \times 10 =$

A 66 B 54 C 60 D 16

058

$1 \times 10 =$

A 1 B 5 C 100 D 10

059

$10 \times 7 =$

A 70 B 77 C 63 D 71

060

$10 \times 10 =$

A 100 B 101 C 110 D 111

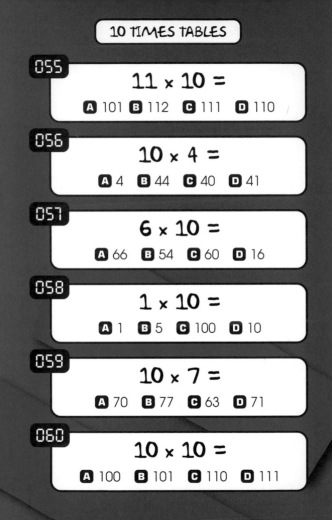

RANDOM SPEED TEST

061

$2 \times 2 =$

A 2 B 22 C 4 D 3

062

$3 \times 3 =$

A 3 B 6 C 9 D 12

063

$4 \times 4 =$

A 16 B 12 C 8 D 4

064

$5 \times 5 =$

A 15 B 20 C 35 D 25

065

$10 \times 10 =$

A 101 B 100 C 110 D 111

066

$6 \times 4 =$

A 12 B 18 C 28 D 24

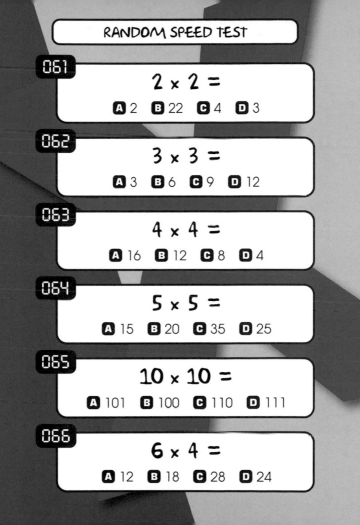

RANDOM SPEED TEST

067

$3 \times 2 =$

A 3 B 5 C 6 D 7

068

$8 \times 4 =$

A 24 B 28 C 26 D 32

069

$7 \times 3 =$

A 14 B 21 C 17 D 23

070

$10 \times 4 =$

A 20 B 40 C 45 D 50

071

$7 \times 2 =$

A 14 B 2 C 7 D 16

072

$11 \times 4 =$

A 36 B 44 C 40 D 48

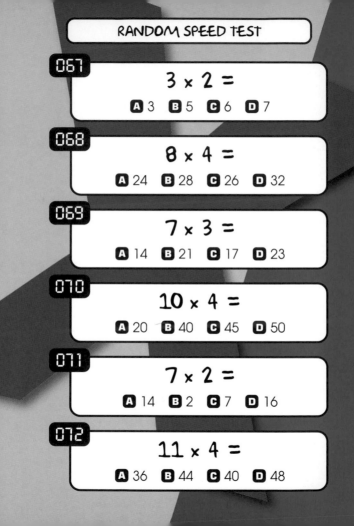

RANDOM SPEED TEST

073

$4 \times 5 =$

A 16 B 18 C 20 D 25

074

$2 \times 3 =$

A 6 B 3 C 2 D 5

075

$8 \times 2 =$

A 12 B 19 C 14 D 16

076

$5 \times 4 =$

A 20 B 15 C 10 D 25

077

$2 \times 5 =$

A 5 B 7 C 10 D 2

078

$4 \times 2 =$

A 2 B 6 C 4 D 8

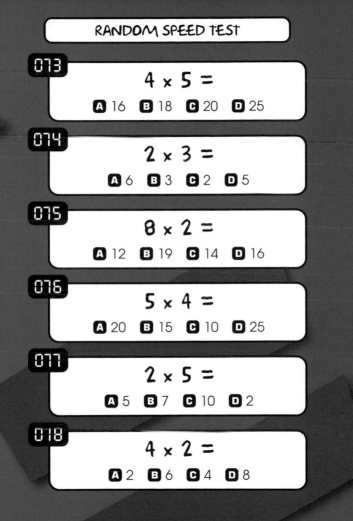

RANDOM SPEED TEST

079

$5 \times 2 =$

A 2 B 5 C 10 D 7

080

$12 \times 3 =$

A 30 B 32 C 34 D 36

081

$6 \times 5 =$

A 25 B 30 C 35 D 40

082

$8 \times 3 =$

A 24 B 16 C 18 D 26

083

$12 \times 10 =$

A 110 B 120 C 112 D 121

084

$9 \times 5 =$

A 35 B 40 C 45 D 30

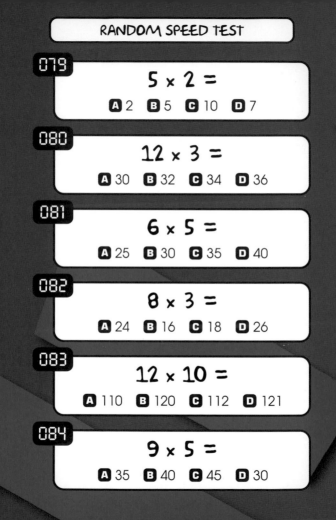

RANDOM SPEED TEST

085

$4 \times 10 =$

A 40 B 4 C 44 D 41

086

$6 \times 2 =$

A 2 B 6 C 12 D 2

087

$11 \times 3 =$

A 11 B 22 C 32 D 33

088

$6 \times 10 =$

A 66 B 16 C 54 D 60

089

$11 \times 10 =$

A 101 B 111 C 110 D 112

090

$3 \times 5 =$

A 15 B 18 C 13 D 12

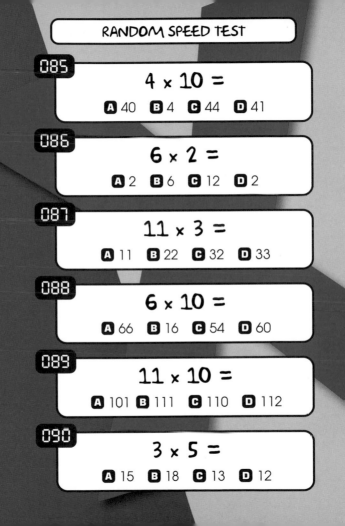

RANDOM SPEED TEST

091

$8 \times 5 =$

A 35 B 40 C 45 D 48

092

$9 \times 10 =$

A 90 B 91 C 99 D 109

093

$10 \times 3 =$

A 10 B 25 C 30 D 36

094

$12 \times 5 =$

A 75 B 65 C 70 D 60

095

$2 \times 4 =$

A 2 B 4 C 6 D 8

096

$11 \times 5 =$

A 55 B 50 C 60 D 65

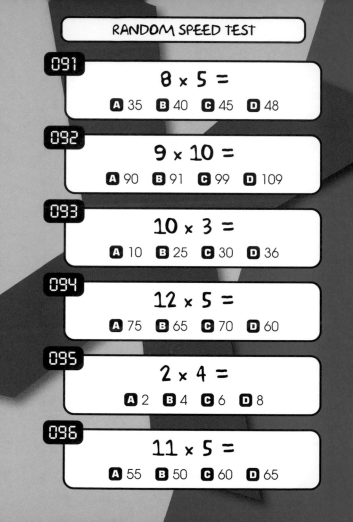

RANDOM SPEED TEST

097

$9 \times 2 =$

A 18 B 16 C 12 D 19

098

$3 \times 4 =$

A 3 B 4 C 8 D 12

099

$10 \times 2 =$

A 20 B 10 C 12 D 22

100

$11 \times 2 =$

A 11 B 20 C 22 D 32

101

$7 \times 10 =$

A 70 B 77 C 63 D 71

102

$9 \times 3 =$

A 24 B 27 C 21 D 19

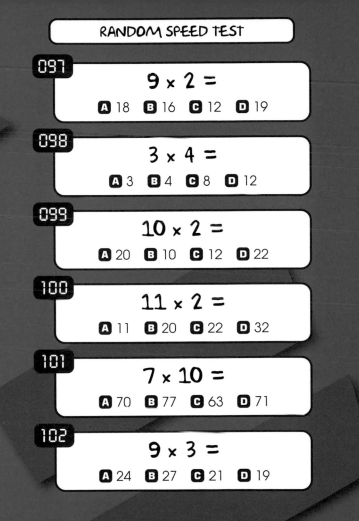

RANDOM SPEED TEST

103

$8 \times 10 =$

A 89 B 81 C 88 D 80

104

$6 \times 3 =$

A 12 B 18 C 20 D 24

105

$7 \times 4 =$

A 21 B 24 C 28 D 32

106

$12 \times 2 =$

A 12 B 14 C 28 D 24

107

$4 \times 3 =$

A 4 B 3 C 7 D 12

108

$5 \times 3 =$

A 15 B 8 C 5 D 25

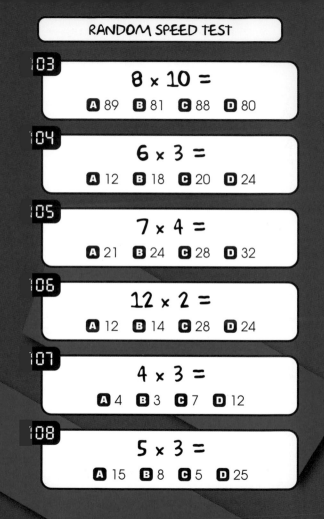

RANDOM SPEED TEST

109

$5 \times 10 =$

A 55 B 51 C 5 D 50

110

$9 \times 4 =$

A 36 B 32 C 34 D 28

111

$7 \times 5 =$

A 30 B 35 C 45 D 42

112

$12 \times 4 =$

A 44 B 48 C 52 D 40

113

$10 \times 5 =$

A 50 B 15 C 45 D 55

114

$12 \times 10 =$

A 110 B 120 C 121 D 60

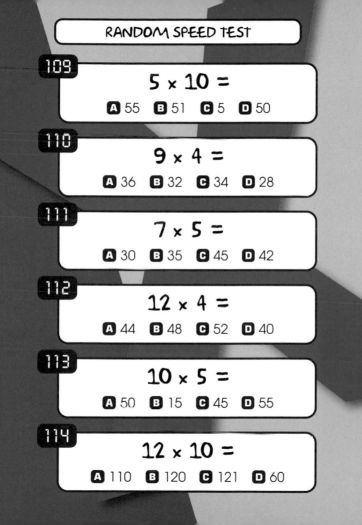

6 TIMES TABLES

These are the ones you know already from the 2, 3, 4, 5 and 10 Times Tables.

$1 \times 6 = 6$
$2 \times 6 = 12$
$3 \times 6 = 18$
$4 \times 6 = 24$
$5 \times 6 = 30$
$10 \times 6 = 60$

See if you can answer a few questions on the 6s with what you already know.

6 TIMES TABLES

115

1 × 6 =

A 4 B 5 C 1 D 6

116

2 × 6 =

A 2 B 3 C 12 D 6

117

3 × 6 =

A 12 B 18 C 16 D 24

118

4 × 6 =

A 18 B 20 C 24 D 16

119

5 × 6 =

A 25 B 30 C 35 D 40

120

10 × 6 =

A 30 B 60 C 45 D 66

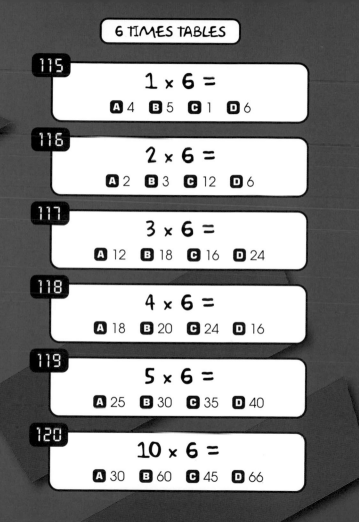

MORE OF THE 6 TIMES TABLES

This is the rest of the 6s — learn these and answer the following questions.

$6 \times 6 = 36$
$7 \times 6 = 42$
$8 \times 6 = 48$
$9 \times 6 = 54$
$11 \times 6 = 66$
$12 \times 6 = 72$

MORE OF THE 6 TIMES TABLES

121

$6 \times 6 =$

A 30 B 40 C 36 D 42

122

$7 \times 6 =$

A 40 B 42 C 36 D 48

123

$8 \times 6 =$

A 40 B 42 C 48 D 38

124

$9 \times 6 =$

A 48 B 52 C 58 D 54

125

$11 \times 6 =$

A 60 B 72 C 66 D 63

126

$12 \times 6 =$

A 72 B 69 C 66 D 75

MORE OF THE 6 TIMES TABLES

27

What are five sixes?

A 18 B 36 C 30 D 42

28

How many sixes are in twenty-four?

A 5 B 4 C 6 D 7

29

What are six sixes?

A 36 B 18 C 42 D 30

30

How many sixes are in forty-eight?

A 6 B 7 C 8 D 9

31

What are nine sixes?

A 66 B 54 C 48 D 42

32

Multiply seven by six

A 72 B 48 C 54 D 42

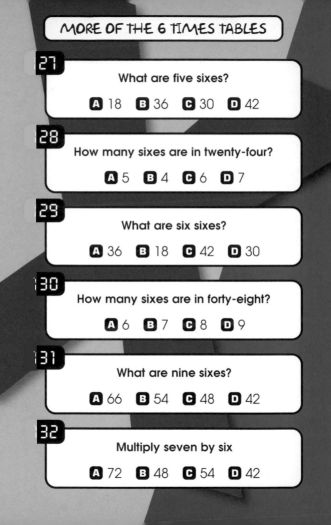

6 TIMES TABLE RECAP

Have a look at the complete 6s and answer the questions afterwards.

$1 \times 6 = 6$

$2 \times 6 = 12$

$3 \times 6 = 18$

$4 \times 6 = 24$

$5 \times 6 = 30$

$6 \times 6 = 36$

$7 \times 6 = 42$

$8 \times 6 = 48$

$9 \times 6 = 54$

$10 \times 6 = 60$

$11 \times 6 = 66$

$12 \times 6 = 72$

6 TIMES TABLE RECAP

133

$1 \times 6 =$

A 6 B 5 C 4 D 1

134

$2 \times 6 =$

A 2 B 12 C 6 D 14

135

$3 \times 6 =$

A 12 B 18 C 16 D 24

136

$4 \times 6 =$

A 24 B 20 C 18 D 16

137

$5 \times 6 =$

A 25 B 30 C 35 D 40

138

$6 \times 6 =$

A 30 B 36 C 40 D 42

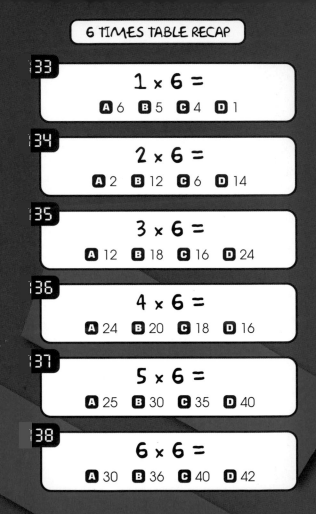

6 TIMES TABLE RECAP

139

$7 \times 6 =$

A 40 B 36 C 42 D 48

140

$8 \times 6 =$

A 38 B 42 C 40 D 48

141

$9 \times 6 =$

A 48 B 52 C 54 D 56

142

$10 \times 6 =$

A 30 B 45 C 60 D 66

143

$11 \times 6 =$

A 66 B 60 C 72 D 63

144

$12 \times 6 =$

A 66 B 69 C 70 D 72

7 TIMES TABLES

These are the ones you know already from the 2, 3, 4, 5, 6 and 10 Times Tables.

$1 \times 7 = 7$
$2 \times 7 = 14$
$3 \times 7 = 21$
$4 \times 7 = 28$
$5 \times 7 = 35$
$6 \times 7 = 42$
$10 \times 7 = 70$

See if you can answer a few questions on the 7s with what you already know.

7 TIMES TABLES

145

$$1 \times 7 =$$

A 1 B 9 C 8 D 7

146

$$2 \times 7 =$$

A 9 B 14 C 12 D 16

147

$$3 \times 7 =$$

A 14 B 21 C 18 D 22

148

$$4 \times 7 =$$

A 24 B 27 C 28 D 21

149

$$5 \times 7 =$$

A 30 B 35 C 40 D 45

150

$$6 \times 7 =$$

A 35 B 40 C 48 D 42

7 TIMES TABLES

151

$$10 \times 7 =$$

A 35 **B** 56 **C** 70 **D** 10

152

What are five sevens?

A 21 **B** 28 **C** 35 **D** 42

153

Multiply six by seven

A 70 **B** 28 **C** 35 **D** 42

154

How many sevens are in twenty-eight?

A 4 **B** 5 **C** 6 **D** 7

155

What are two sevens?

A 14 **B** 15 **C** 18 **D** 24

156

Multiply three by seven

A 18 **B** 28 **C** 21 **D** 14

MORE OF THE 7 TIMES TABLES

This is the rest of the 7s — learn these and answer the following questions.

$7 \times 7 = 49$
$8 \times 7 = 56$
$9 \times 7 = 63$
$11 \times 7 = 77$
$12 \times 7 = 84$

MORE OF THE 7 TIMES TABLES

157

$7 \times 7 =$

A 42 B 45 C 49 D 77

158

$8 \times 7 =$

A 56 B 53 C 54 D 48

159

$9 \times 7 =$

A 54 B 57 C 62 D 63

160

$11 \times 7 =$

A 61 B 77 C 70 D 84

161

$12 \times 7 =$

A 77 B 91 C 88 D 84

162

What are seven sevens?

A 28 B 35 C 49 D 42

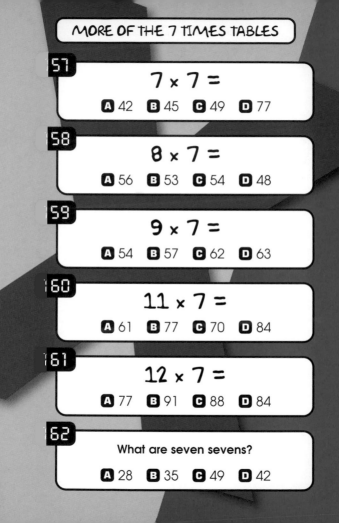

MORE OF THE 7 TIMES TABLES

163

Multiply seven by eight

A 64 B 42 C 49 D 56

164

How many sevens are in seventy-seven?

A 9 B 11 C 10 D 12

165

What are twelve sevens?

A 70 B 84 C 77 D 54

166

Multiply nine by seven

A 63 B 70 C 77 D 36

167

How many sevens are in fourteen?

A 4 B 2 C 3 D 5

168

What are six sevens?

A 24 B 48 C 42 D 56

7 TIMES TABLE RECAP

Here are all the 7s again.
Take a quick look and answer all the following questions.

1 × 7 = 7
2 × 7 = 14
3 × 7 = 21
4 × 7 = 28
5 × 7 = 35
6 × 7 = 42
7 × 7 = 49
8 × 7 = 56
9 × 7 = 63
10 × 7 = 70
11 × 7 = 77
12 × 7 = 84

7 TIMES TABLE RECAP

169

$1 \times 7 =$

A 7 B 1 C 8 D 9

170

$2 \times 7 =$

A 9 B 16 C 12 D 14

171

$3 \times 7 =$

A 21 B 18 C 14 D 22

172

$4 \times 7 =$

A 24 B 27 C 28 D 21

173

$5 \times 7 =$

A 30 B 45 C 40 D 35

174

$6 \times 7 =$

A 35 B 40 C 42 D 48

7 TIMES TABLE RECAP

175

7 × 7 =

A 42 B 45 C 77 D 49

176

8 × 7 =

A 48 B 56 C 53 D 57

177

9 × 7 =

A 63 B 57 C 62 D 54

178

10 × 7 =

A 35 B 70 C 77 D 10

179

11 × 7 =

A 61 B 70 C 77 D 84

180

12 × 7 =

A 84 B 77 C 88 D 91

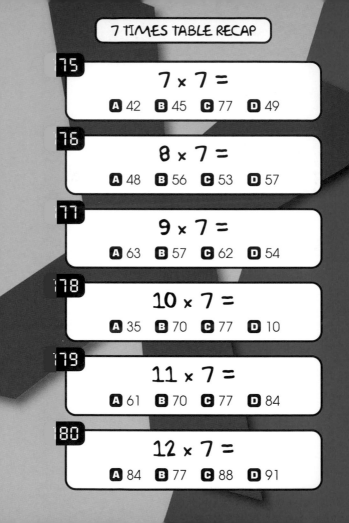

8 TIMES TABLES

These are the ones you know already from the 2, 3, 4, 5, 6, 7 and 10 Times Tables.

$1 \times 8 = 8$

$2 \times 8 = 16$

$3 \times 8 = 24$

$4 \times 8 = 32$

$5 \times 8 = 40$

$6 \times 8 = 48$

$7 \times 8 = 56$

$10 \times 8 = 80$

See if you can answer a few questions on the 8s with what you already know.

8 TIMES TABLES

181

1 x 8 =

A 1 B 18 C 8 D 9

182

2 x 8 =

A 28 B 18 C 12 D 16

183

3 x 8 =

A 22 B 18 C 26 D 24

184

4 x 8 =

A 28 B 24 C 32 D 34

185

5 x 8 =

A 40 B 36 C 30 D 44

186

6 x 8 =

A 36 B 48 C 42 D 40

8 TIMES TABLES

187

$7 \times 8 =$

A 56 B 48 C 40 D 64

188

$10 \times 8 =$

A 64 B 56 C 80 D 88

189

What are five eights?

A 21 B 28 C 42 D 40

190

Multiply six by eight

A 42 B 28 C 36 D 48

191

How many eights are in thirty-two?

A 4 B 5 C 6 D 7

192

Multiply three by eight

A 24 B 28 C 18 D 14

MORE OF THE 8 TIMES TABLES

This is the rest of the 8s — learn these, then cover them up and answer the following questions.

$8 \times 8 = 64$
$9 \times 8 = 72$
$11 \times 8 = 88$
$12 \times 8 = 96$

193

$8 \times 8 =$

A 48 B 53 C 56 D 64

194

$9 \times 8 =$

A 72 B 56 C 64 D 74

195

$11 \times 8 =$

A 81 B 80 C 88 D 84

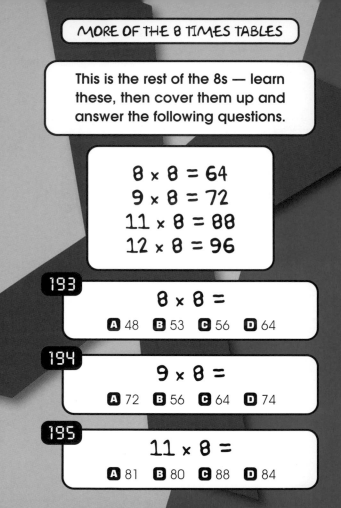

MORE OF THE 8 TIMES TABLES

196

$12 \times 8 =$

A 96 B 94 C 88 D 98

197

Multiply nine by eight

A 64 B 72 C 80 D 56

198

What are eight eights?

A 56 B 48 C 42 D 64

199

Multiply eleven by eight

A 72 B 88 C 80 D 86

200

What are twelve eights?

A 80 B 88 C 96 D 94

201

How many eights are in seventy-two?

A 12 B 10 C 11 D 9

8 TIMES TABLE RECAP

Here's stuff you know already so you should be able to speed through these.

$1 \times 8 = 8$
$2 \times 8 = 16$
$3 \times 8 = 24$
$4 \times 8 = 32$
$5 \times 8 = 40$
$6 \times 8 = 48$
$7 \times 8 = 56$
$8 \times 8 = 64$
$9 \times 8 = 72$
$10 \times 8 = 80$
$11 \times 8 = 88$
$12 \times 8 = 96$

8 TIMES TABLE RECAP

202

$1 \times 8 =$

A 9 B 4 C 6 D 8

203

$2 \times 8 =$

A 16 B 12 C 18 D 22

204

$3 \times 8 =$

A 16 B 20 C 18 D 24

205

$4 \times 8 =$

A 32 B 36 C 28 D 26

206

$5 \times 8 =$

A 48 B 40 C 42 D 44

207

$6 \times 8 =$

A 42 B 48 C 54 D 52

8 TIMES TABLE RECAP

208

$7 \times 8 =$

A 56 B 52 C 58 D 60

209

$8 \times 8 =$

A 62 B 64 C 58 D 56

210

$9 \times 8 =$

A 84 B 79 C 81 D 72

211

$10 \times 8 =$

A 64 B 88 C 80 D 92

212

$11 \times 8 =$

A 80 B 88 C 90 D 99

213

$12 \times 8 =$

A 88 B 98 C 96 D 102

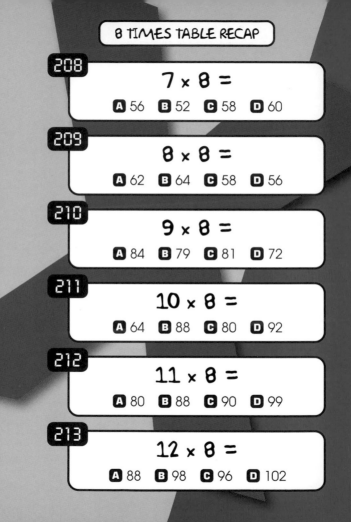

9 TIMES TABLES

These are the ones you know already from the 2, 3, 4, 5, 6, 7, 8 and 10 Times Tables.

$1 \times 9 = 9$

$2 \times 9 = 18$

$3 \times 9 = 27$

$4 \times 9 = 36$

$5 \times 9 = 45$

$6 \times 9 = 54$

$7 \times 9 = 63$

$8 \times 9 = 72$

$10 \times 9 = 90$

See if you can answer a few questions on the 9s with what you already know.

9 TIMES TABLES

214

$1 \times 9 =$

A 1 B 9 C 8 D 10

215

$2 \times 9 =$

A 17 B 18 C 12 D 16

216

$3 \times 9 =$

A 24 B 18 C 27 D 29

217

$4 \times 9 =$

A 32 B 36 C 24 D 34

218

$5 \times 9 =$

A 44 B 36 C 45 D 40

219

$6 \times 9 =$

A 48 B 52 C 45 D 54

9 TIMES TABLES

220

$7 \times 9 =$

A 54 B 72 C 63 D 79

221

$8 \times 9 =$

A 72 B 80 C 81 D 79

222

$10 \times 9 =$

A 109 B 70 C 90 D 80

223

What are eight nines?

A 81 B 72 C 99 D 89

224

Multiply six by nine

A 54 B 45 C 36 D 48

225

How many nines are in sixty-three?

A 8 B 5 C 7 D 6

MORE OF THE 9 TIMES TABLES

This is the rest of the 9s — learn these, then cover them up and answer the following questions.

$9 \times 9 = 81$
$11 \times 9 = 99$
$12 \times 9 = 108$

226

$9 \times 9 =$

A 80 **B** 81 **C** 72 **D** 63

227

$11 \times 9 =$

A 84 **B** 91 **C** 88 **D** 99

228

$12 \times 9 =$

A 108 **B** 94 **C** 96 **D** 91

MORE OF THE 9 TIMES TABLES

229

Multiply twelve by nine

A 99 B 108 C 106 D 104

230

How many nines are in eighty-one?

A 10 B 9 C 8 D 7

231

Multiply eleven by nine

A 99 B 88 C 108 D 80

232

What are twelve nines?

A 72 B 108 C 81 D 90

233

How many nines in eighty-one?

A 6 B 9 C 7 D 8

234

What are eleven nines?

A 72 B 81 C 99 D 108

9 TIMES TABLE RECAP

Here's stuff you know already so you should be able to speed through these.

$1 \times 9 = 9$

$2 \times 9 = 18$

$3 \times 9 = 27$

$4 \times 9 = 36$

$5 \times 9 = 45$

$6 \times 9 = 54$

$7 \times 9 = 63$

$8 \times 9 = 72$

$9 \times 9 = 81$

$10 \times 9 = 90$

$11 \times 9 = 99$

$12 \times 9 = 108$

9 TIMES TABLE RECAP

235

$1 \times 9 =$

A 18 B 19 C 10 D 9

236

$2 \times 9 =$

A 16 B 19 C 18 D 21

237

$3 \times 9 =$

A 24 B 26 C 27 D 29

238

$4 \times 9 =$

A 36 B 28 C 39 D 45

239

$5 \times 9 =$

A 54 B 48 C 52 D 45

240

$6 \times 9 =$

A 69 B 60 C 63 D 54

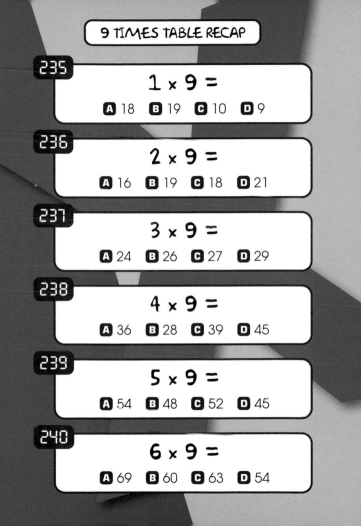

9 TIMES TABLE RECAP

241

$7 \times 9 =$

A 59 B 63 C 70 D 79

242

$8 \times 9 =$

A 78 B 72 C 84 D 89

243

$9 \times 9 =$

A 78 B 90 C 81 D 99

244

$10 \times 9 =$

A 99 B 90 C 108 D 109

245

$11 \times 9 =$

A 119 B 108 C 109 D 99

246

$12 \times 9 =$

A 118 B 109 C 108 D 129

10 TIMES TABLES

These are the ones you know already from the 2, 3, 4, 5, 6, 7, 8, 9 and 10 Times Tables.

$1 \times 10 = 10$
$2 \times 10 = 20$
$3 \times 10 = 30$
$4 \times 10 = 40$
$5 \times 10 = 50$
$6 \times 10 = 60$
$7 \times 10 = 70$
$8 \times 10 = 80$
$9 \times 10 = 90$
$10 \times 10 = 100$

See if you can answer a few questions on the 10s with what you already know.

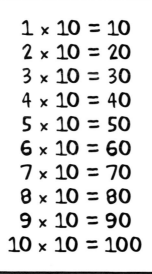

10 TIMES TABLES

247

$1 \times 10 =$

A 1 B 11 C 10 D 9

248

$2 \times 10 =$

A 10 B 15 C 21 D 20

249

$3 \times 10 =$

A 30 B 3 C 33 D 10

250

$4 \times 10 =$

A 40 B 14 C 4 D 44

251

$5 \times 10 =$

A 10 B 51 C 50 D 5

252

$6 \times 10 =$

A 66 B 10 C 60 D 6

10 TIMES TABLES

253

$7 \times 10 =$

A 70 B 63 C 90 D 71

254

$8 \times 10 =$

A 72 B 10 C 81 D 80

255

$9 \times 10 =$

A 19 B 90 C 109 D 1

256

$10 \times 10 =$

A 109 B 90 C 80 D 100

257

What are seven tens?

A 50 B 40 C 70 D 80

258

Multiply six by ten?

A 40 B 66 C 80 D 60

MORE OF THE 10 TIMES TABLES

This is the rest of the 10s — learn these, then cover them up and answer the following questions.

$11 \times 10 = 110$
$12 \times 10 = 120$

259

$11 \times 10 =$

A 99 **B** 110 **C** 100 **D** 111

260

What are twelve tens?

A 90 **B** 120 **C** 110 **D** 100

261

How many tens are in one hundred and twenty?

A 12 **B** 9 **C** 11 **D** 10

10 TIMES TABLE RECAP

Here's stuff you know already so you should be able to speed through these.

$1 \times 10 = 10$

$2 \times 10 = 20$

$3 \times 10 = 30$

$4 \times 10 = 40$

$5 \times 10 = 50$

$6 \times 10 = 60$

$7 \times 10 = 70$

$8 \times 10 = 80$

$9 \times 10 = 90$

$10 \times 10 = 100$

$11 \times 10 = 110$

$12 \times 10 = 120$

10 TIMES TABLE RECAP

262

$1 \times 10 =$

A 1 B 10 C 5 D 100

263

$2 \times 10 =$

A 2 B 10 C 20 D 22

264

$3 \times 10 =$

A 30 B 33 C 27 D 3

265

$4 \times 10 =$

A 4 B 41 C 44 D 40

266

$5 \times 10 =$

A 50 B 51 C 55 D 5

267

$6 \times 10 =$

A 66 B 54 C 60 D 16

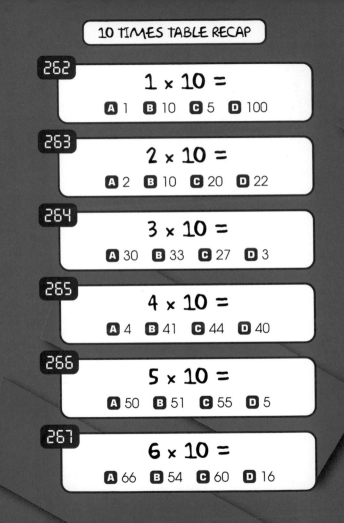

10 TIMES TABLE RECAP

268

$7 \times 10 =$

A 63 B 77 C 71 D 70

269

$8 \times 10 =$

A 88 B 81 C 80 D 89

270

$9 \times 10 =$

A 109 B 91 C 99 D 90

271

$10 \times 10 =$

A 101 B 100 C 110 D 111

272

$11 \times 10 =$

A 110 B 101 C 111 D 112

273

$12 \times 10 =$

A 110 B 120 C 112 D 121

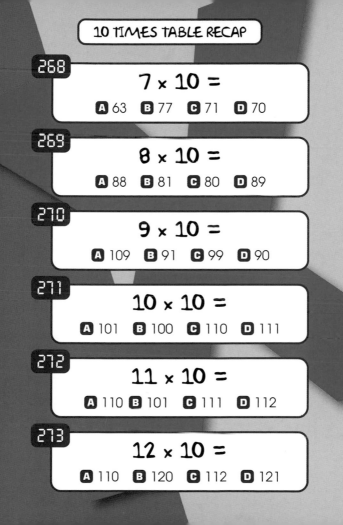

11 and 12 TIMES TABLES

You already know most of the 11s and 12s from the 2, 3, 4, 5, 6, 7, 8, 9 and 10 Times Tables. Here are the 11s.

$1 \times 11 = 11$
$2 \times 11 = 22$
$3 \times 11 = 33$
$4 \times 11 = 44$
$5 \times 11 = 55$
$6 \times 11 = 66$
$7 \times 11 = 77$
$8 \times 11 = 88$
$9 \times 11 = 99$
$10 \times 11 = 110$

See if you can answer a few questions on the 11s with what you already know.

11 and 12 TIMES TABLES

274

$1 \times 11 =$

A 1 B 10 C 11 D 12

275

$2 \times 11 =$

A 22 B 15 C 20 D 21

276

$3 \times 11 =$

A 3 B 30 C 33 D 10

277

$4 \times 11 =$

A 4 B 14 C 40 D 44

278

$5 \times 11 =$

A 50 B 51 C 10 D 55

279

$6 \times 11 =$

A 16 B 6 C 66 D 60

280

$7 \times 11 =$

A 77   B 63   C 70   D 71

281

$8 \times 11 =$

A 72   B 88   C 81   D 79

282

$9 \times 11 =$

A 99   B 19   C 109   D 90

283

$10 \times 11 =$

A 109   B 90   C 110   D 100

284

What are seven elevens?

A 55   B 117   C 70   D 77

285

Multiply six by eleven?

A 64   B 60   C 77   D 66

Here are the 12s that you have learnt before.

1 × 12 = 12
2 × 12 = 24
3 × 12 = 36
4 × 12 = 48
5 × 12 = 60
6 × 12 = 72
7 × 12 = 84
8 × 12 = 96
9 × 12 = 108
10 × 12 = 120

See if you can answer a few questions on the 12s with what you already know.

11 and 12 TIMES TABLES

286

$1 \times 12 =$

A 12 B 11 C 112 D 21

287

$2 \times 12 =$

A 24 B 22 C 28 D 26

288

$3 \times 12 =$

A 32 B 42 C 38 D 36

289

$4 \times 12 =$

A 48 B 40 C 36 D 50

290

$5 \times 12 =$

A 58 B 62 C 60 D 64

291

$6 \times 12 =$

A 72 B 70 C 68 D 76

11 and 12 TIMES TABLES

292

$7 \times 12 =$

A 80 B 84 C 76 D 72

293

$8 \times 12 =$

A 88 B 92 C 94 D 96

294

$9 \times 12 =$

A 104 B 108 C 102 D 98

295

$10 \times 12 =$

A 110 B 112 C 120 D 118

296

How many twelves in one hundred and eight?

A 6 B 7 C 8 D 9

297

Multiply six by eleven?

A 72 B 60 C 77 D 66

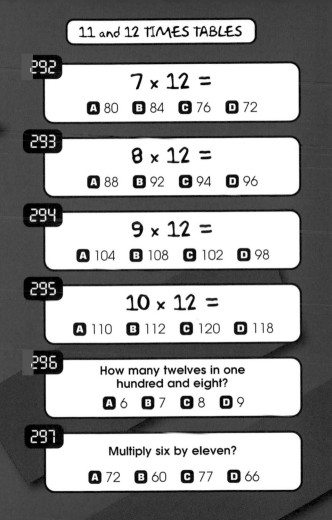

11 and 12 TIMES TABLES

This is the rest of the 11s and 12s — learn these, then cover them up and answer the following questions.

$$11 \times 11 = 121$$
$$12 \times 11 = 132$$
$$12 \times 12 = 144$$

298

$11 \times 11 =$

A 121 B 110 C 111 D 100

299

$12 \times 11 =$

A 121 B 120 C 122 D 132

300

$12 \times 12 =$

A 144 B 136 C 140 D 132

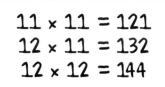

11 TIMES TABLE RECAP

Here's stuff you know already so you should be able to speed through these.

1	×	11	=	11
2	×	11	=	22
3	×	11	=	33
4	×	11	=	44
5	×	11	=	55
6	×	11	=	66
7	×	11	=	77
8	×	11	=	88
9	×	11	=	99
10	×	11	=	110
11	×	11	=	121
12	×	11	=	132

11 TIMES TABLE RECAP

301

$1 \times 11 =$

A 22 B 11 C 13 D 21

302

$2 \times 11 =$

A 20 B 22 C 24 D 12

303

$3 \times 11 =$

A 33 B 36 C 31 D 30

304

$4 \times 11 =$

A 42 B 44 C 41 D 40

305

$5 \times 11 =$

A 45 B 51 C 52 D 55

306

$6 \times 11 =$

A 60 B 61 C 66 D 72

11 TIMES TABLE RECAP

307

$7 \times 11 =$

A 70 B 77 C 72 D 76

308

$8 \times 11 =$

A 81 B 89 C 88 D 91

309

$9 \times 11 =$

A 91 B 99 C 98 D 109

310

$10 \times 11 =$

A 101 B 110 C 111 D 121

311

$11 \times 11 =$

A 111 B 120 C 121 D 122

312

$12 \times 11 =$

A 121 B 132 C 131 D 130

12 TIMES TABLE RECAP

Here's stuff you know already so you should be able to speed through these.

1 × 12 = 12
2 × 12 = 24
3 × 12 = 36
4 × 12 = 48
5 × 12 = 60
6 × 12 = 72
7 × 12 = 84
8 × 12 = 96
9 × 12 = 108
10 × 12 = 120
11 × 12 = 132
12 × 12 = 144

12 TIMES TABLE RECAP

313

$1 \times 12 =$

A 112 B 11 C 12 D 21

314

$2 \times 12 =$

A 18 B 22 C 20 D 24

315

$3 \times 12 =$

A 32 B 38 C 36 D 42

316

$4 \times 12 =$

A 48 B 40 C 36 D 50

317

$5 \times 12 =$

A 58 B 62 C 60 D 64

318

$6 \times 12 =$

A 68 B 72 C 74 D 76

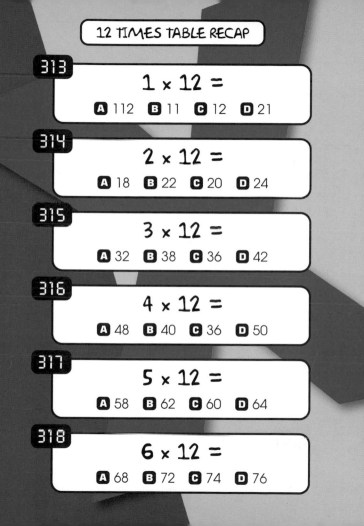

12 TIMES TABLE RECAP

319

$7 \times 12 =$

A 84 B 80 C 76 D 72

320

$8 \times 12 =$

A 88 B 92 C 96 D 94

321

$9 \times 12 =$

A 104 B 108 C 102 D 98

322

$10 \times 12 =$

A 110 B 112 C 118 D 120

323

$11 \times 12 =$

A 132 B 124 C 116 D 112

324

$12 \times 12 =$

A 122 B 144 C 136 D 148

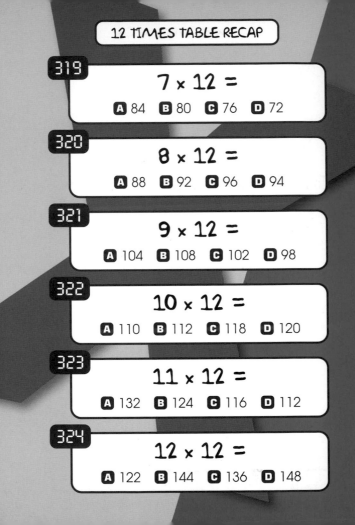

MEGA TEST

325

$3 \times 3 =$

A 3 B 9 C 6 D 12

326

$4 \times 4 =$

A 16 B 12 C 8 D 4

327

$5 \times 5 =$

A 15 B 25 C 20 D 35

328

$6 \times 6 =$

A 30 B 36 C 40 D 42

329

$7 \times 7 =$

A 42 B 45 C 49 D 77

330

$8 \times 8 =$

A 62 B 72 C 58 D 64

331

$9 \times 9 =$

A 78 B 90 C 81 D 99

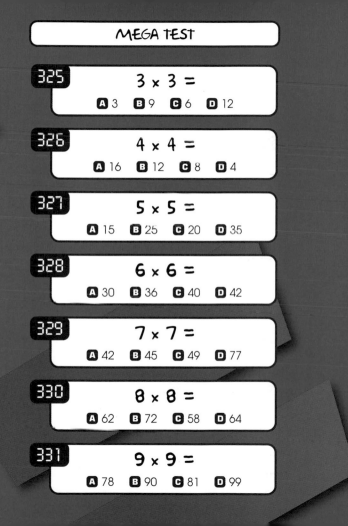

MEGA TEST

332

$10 \times 10 =$

A 110 B 101 C 100 D 111

333

$11 \times 11 =$

A 121 B 120 C 111 D 122

334

$12 \times 12 =$

A 122 B 136 C 140 D 144

335

$6 \times 4 =$

A 12 B 18 C 28 D 24

336

$3 \times 2 =$

A 3 B 6 C 5 D 2

337

$8 \times 4 =$

A 28 B 32 C 26 D 24

338

$7 \times 3 =$

A 14 B 17 C 21 D 23

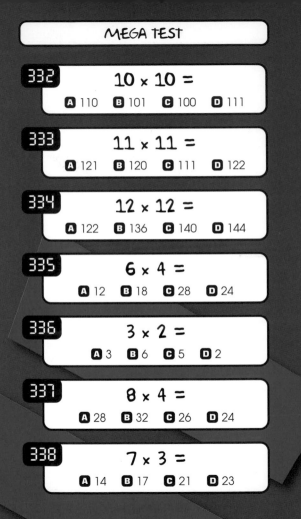

MEGA TEST

339 $7 \times 2 =$

A 7　B 14　C 9　D 16

340 $11 \times 4 =$

A 36　B 40　C 48　D 44

341 $4 \times 5 =$

A 16　B 18　C 20　D 14

342 $11 \times 12 =$

A 116　B 124　C 132　D 112

343 $7 \times 9 =$

A 59　B 79　C 70　D 63

344 $8 \times 2 =$

A 16　B 12　C 14　D 19

345 $8 \times 7 =$

A 56　B 53　C 48　D 57

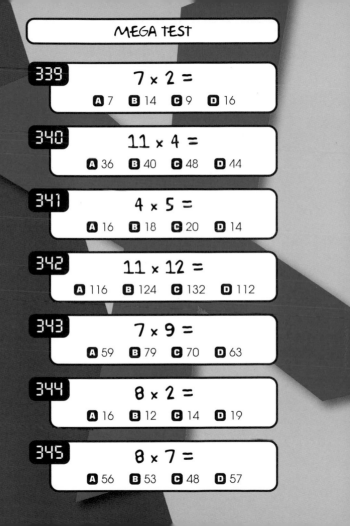

MEGA TEST

346 $7 \times 11 =$

A 70 B 71 C 77 D 72

347 $4 \times 2 =$

A 4 B 6 C 8 D 2

348 $11 \times 6 =$

A 66 B 60 C 72 D 63

349 $9 \times 12 =$

A 98 B 104 C 102 D 108

350 $7 \times 12 =$

A 80 B 84 C 76 D 72

351 $5 \times 2 =$

A 7 B 5 C 2 D 10

352 $12 \times 3 =$

A 30 B 32 C 36 D 38

MEGA TEST

353 8 x 9 =

A 89 B 78 C 84 D 72

354 6 x 5 =

A 25 B 30 C 35 D 40

355 8 x 3 =

A 16 B 24 C 18 D 26

356 11 x 8 =

A 88 B 80 C 90 D 99

357 12 x 6 =

A 66 B 72 C 78 D 75

358 9 x 8 =

A 81 B 79 C 72 D 84

359 4 x 7 =

A 28 B 27 C 24 D 21

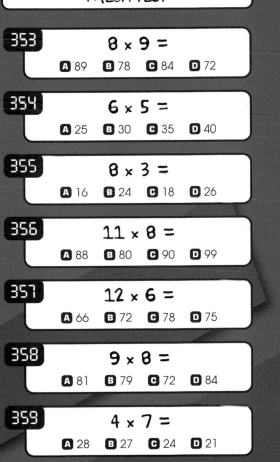

MEGA TEST

360 $12 \times 10 =$

A 110 B 112 C 121 D 120

361 $9 \times 5 =$

A 45 B 40 C 35 D 30

362 $9 \times 7 =$

A 54 B 57 C 63 D 65

363 $4 \times 10 =$

A 4 B 10 C 44 D 40

364 $7 \times 8 =$

A 52 B 54 C 56 D 60

365 $12 \times 9 =$

A 129 B 109 C 119 D 108

366 $2 \times 11 =$

A 20 B 22 C 24 D 12

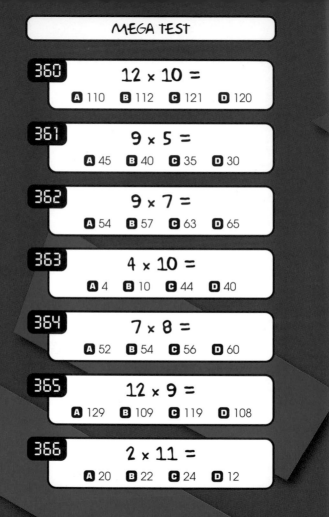

MEGA TEST

367 6 x 2 =

A 12 B 16 C 6 D 2

369 11 x 3 =

A 11 B 33 C 22 D 32

369 7 x 6 =

A 40 B 36 C 42 D 48

370 6 x 10 =

A 60 B 66 C 54 D 16

371 6 x 8 =

A 42 B 26 C 48 D 52

372 11 x 10 =

A 101 B 112 C 111 D 110

373 8 x 12 =

A 88 B 92 C 94 D 96

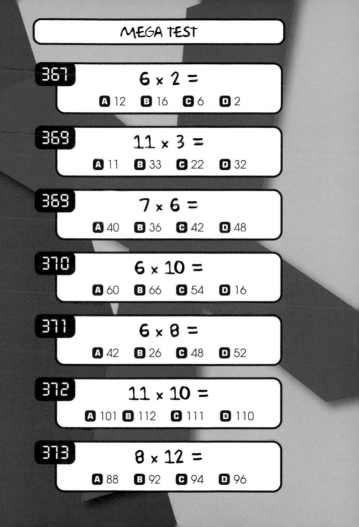

MEGA TEST

374

$3 \times 5 =$

A 18   B 13   C 15   D 12

375

$12 \times 7 =$

A 84   B 77   C 88   D 91

376

$4 \times 8 =$

A 36   B 32   C 28   D 26

377

$8 \times 5 =$

A 40   B 42   C 45   D 48

378

$9 \times 10 =$

A 99   B 91   C 90   D 109

379

$12 \times 11 =$

A 121   B 130   C 131   D 132

380

$10 \times 3 =$

A 10   B 20   C 25   D 30

MEGA TEST

381 $8 \times 6 =$

A 48 B 42 C 40 D 38

382 $12 \times 5 =$

A 60 B 65 C 70 D 75

383 $4 \times 9 =$

A 28 B 45 C 39 D 36

384 $11 \times 5 =$

A 55 B 45 C 60 D 65

385 $9 \times 2 =$

A 11 B 16 C 18 D 19

386 $4 \times 11 =$

A 44 B 42 C 41 D 40

387 $10 \times 2 =$

A 10 B 20 C 12 D 22

MEGA TEST

388

$6 \times 7 =$

A 35 B 40 C 48 D 42

389

$9 \times 11 =$

A 91 B 99 C 108 D 109

390

$11 \times 2 =$

A 11 B 20 C 22 D 32

391

$6 \times 9 =$

A 69 B 60 C 63 D 54

392

$7 \times 10 =$

A 63 B 77 C 71 D 70

393

$11 \times 7 =$

A 77 B 70 C 117 D 84

394

$9 \times 3 =$

A 19 B 24 C 21 D 27

MEGA TEST

395 $8 \times 10 =$

A 80 B 81 C 88 D 89

396 $4 \times 12 =$

A 36 B 48 C 40 D 50

397 $6 \times 3 =$

A 12 B 18 C 20 D 24

398 $7 \times 4 =$

A 28 B 24 C 22 D 32

399 $12 \times 2 =$

A 12 B 24 C 14 D 28

400 $4 \times 3 =$

A 4 B 3 C 7 D 12

401 $6 \times 12 =$

A 68 B 70 C 72 D 76

MEGA TEST

402 $6 \times 11 =$

A 60 B 66 C 61 D 72

403 $8 \times 11 =$

A 81 B 89 C 88 D 91

404 $9 \times 4 =$

A 28 B 36 C 34 D 32

405 $7 \times 5 =$

A 40 B 35 C 45 D 42

406 $12 \times 4 =$

A 52 B 44 C 48 D 40

407 $10 \times 5 =$

A 15 B 50 C 45 D 55

408 $4 \times 6 =$

A 18 B 20 C 24 D 16

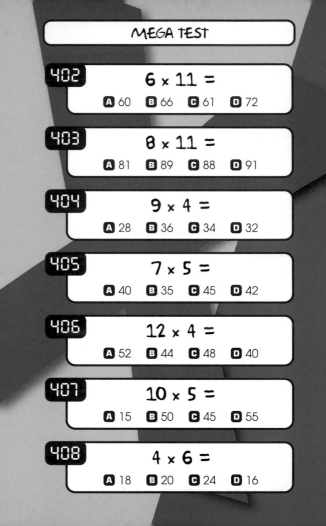

MEGA TEST

409 $12 \times 8 =$

A 88 B 102 C 98 D 96

410 $9 \times 6 =$

A 48 B 52 C 54 D 56

411 $11 \times 9 =$

A 99 B 108 C 109 D 119

412 $8 \times 7 =$

A 48 B 53 C 56 D 57

413 $9 \times 6 =$

A 48 B 54 C 52 D 56

414 $11 \times 12 =$

A 132 B 124 C 116 D 112

415 $5 \times 12 =$

A 58 B 62 C 60 D 64

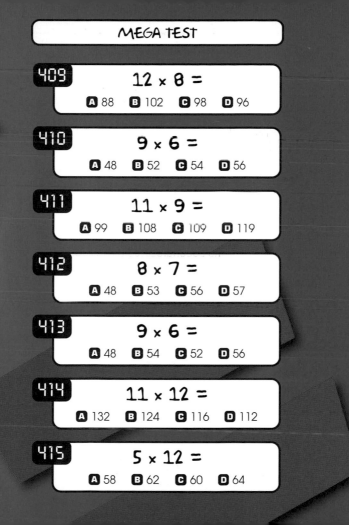

Other Titles

There are many other exciting quiz and puzzle books in the IntelliQuest range, and your QUIZMO electronic unit knows the answers to them all!

You can order from your local IntelliQuest stockist or on-line bookseller.

For a full listing of current titles (and ISBN numbers) see:

www.thelagoongroup.com/intelliquest

LAGOON BOOKS